POSTCARDS · FROM ·

South Africa

Zoë Dawson

RSVP®

RAINTREE
STECK-VAUGHN
PUBLISHERS
The Steck-Vaughn Company

Austin, Texas

Published by Raintree Steck-Vaughn Publishers, an imprint of Steck-Vaughn Company

A *ZOË BOOK*

Editors: Kath Davies, Helene Resky
Design: Jan Sterling, Sterling Associates
Map: Gecko Limited
Production: Grahame Griffiths.

Library of Congress Cataloging-in-Publication Data

Dawson, Zoë.
    South Africa / Zoë Dawson.
        p. cm. — (Postcards from)
    Includes index.
    ISBN 0-8172-4015-2 (lib. binding)
    ISBN 0-8172-4236-8 (softcover)
    1. South Africa — Description and travel — Juvenile literature.
  I. Title. II. Series.
  DT1719.D39 1996
  968–dc20   95–16714
                                                           CIP
                                                             AC

Printed and bound in the United States
    4 5 6 7 8 9 0 WZ 02 01 00

Photographic acknowledgments

The publishers wish to acknowledge, with thanks, the following photographic sources:

The Hutchison Library / Ingrid Hudson - title page; / Liba Taylor 10; / Robert Aberman 26; Robert Harding Picture Library / J. Lightfoot 18; Impact Photos / Caroline Salguero - cover bl, 28; / Rhonda Klevansky 20; / Gideon Mendel 22; / Piers Cavendish 24; Zefa - cover tl & r, 6, 8, 12, 14, 16.

The publishers have made every effort to trace the copyright holders, but if they have inadvertently overlooked any, they will be pleased to make the necessary arrangement at the first opportunity.

Contents

All the words that appear in **bold** are explained in the Glossary on page 30.

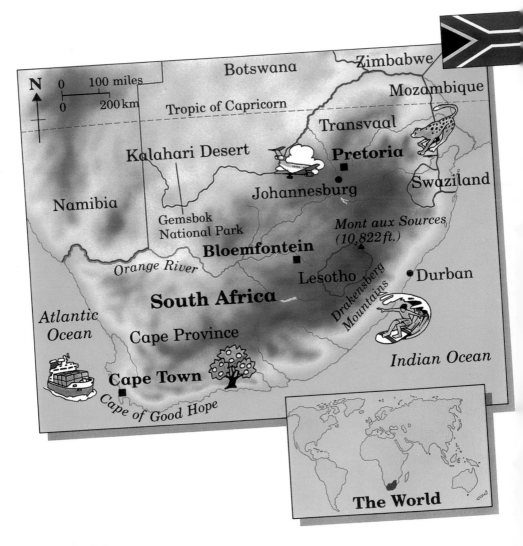

A big map of South Africa
and a small map of the world

Dear Blanca,

You can see South Africa in red on the small map. It is a long way from home. South Africa is much smaller than the United States. It is about twice the size of Texas.

Love,

Sara

P.S. Dad says that fewer people live in South Africa than in the United States. About half the people in South Africa live in towns and cities.

The city of Cape Town below
Table Mountain

Dear Lisa,

We are in Cape Town. It is one of the three **capital** cities of South Africa. The plane took more than 14 hours to fly here from Miami. We saw the African coast and the Atlantic Ocean from the plane.

Your friend,

Darren

P.S. Cape Town is on the coast. Dad says the **cape** is called the Cape of Good Hope. Table Mountain has a flat top, like a table.

A street market in Johannesburg

Dear Philip,

Johannesburg is the biggest city in South Africa. We went shopping here. Dad gave us some South African money called *rand*. Most people here speak English. Some people speak **Afrikaans**.

Love,

Ginny

P.S. Mom says that Dutch people settled here long ago. Afrikaans is based on Dutch. **Native** peoples in South Africa speak many different languages.

A market stand selling fresh fruit
and vegetables

Dear Marianne,

I love the food in South Africa. We went out to lunch today. I had a huge seafood salad. We buy fresh fruit from the market every day. I like the grapes best!

Your friend,

Charlotte

P.S. Dad says that South Africa sells its food all over the world. Some of the fish, fruit, and vegetables are canned. They are loaded onto ships at Cape Town and Durban.

11

The Blue Train

Dear Chris,

Many people here travel by train every day. They go to work in the cities. They are called **commuters**. The Blue Train is famous. I would love to travel on it. We go by plane from city to city.

Yours,

Andre

P.S. Dad says that there are gold mines in South Africa. Heavy **goods** travel by train. There are good roads, too.

The Gemsbok National Park, South Africa

Dear Annie,

We are close to a country called Botswana. This park is on the edge of the Kalahari Desert. The wild animals are **protected** here. I have not seen a lion yet!

Your friend,

David

P.S. Mom says that South Africa has many different kinds of wildflowers. There are many different birds, too.

An Ndebele woman making bead
jewelry in the Transvaal

Dear Tina,

The Ndebele people live here in the Transvaal. The women make brightly colored clothes like these. They also make very beautiful jewelry from tiny beads.

Love,

Kate

P.S. Dad says that the Transvaal is one of the **provinces** in South Africa. Many Dutch farmers called the Boers came to live here more than 150 years ago.

In the Drakensberg Mountains

Dear Chanel,

These are the highest mountains in South Africa. We have come here to see the cave paintings. They were made by the **San** people thousands of years ago.

Yours,

Pat

P.S. Mom says that the highest mountain in South Africa is called Mont aux Sources. It is more than 9,800 feet (3,000 m) high.

At school in Durban

Dear Ray,

We went to school today! The children work hard. They are very quiet in the classroom. Our friend Lewis played in a soccer game for the school in the afternoon.

See you soon,

Lee

P.S. The teacher said that part of South Africa is in the **tropics**. The weather here is hot and damp. Farmers can grow all kinds of **crops**.

On the beach at Durban

Dear Rosie,

We have been swimming for most of the day. It is too hot to sit on the beach for long. Many people come here for vacations. Durban is one of the biggest cities in South Africa.

Love,

Jasmine

P.S. Durban is on the east coast. Dad says that we have been swimming in the Indian Ocean. The harbor is full of big ships that take goods from Africa all over the world.

A rugby game in the Cape Province

Dear Daniel,

People play many different sports here. We have seen sports fields in every town. Most of my friends play soccer every day. South Africans are very good at **rugby** and **cricket**, too.

Yours,

Marie

P.S. Mom says that some people work all the time. They are too poor to take vacations. They sometimes play sports after work.

Carnival in Cape Town

Dear Sasha,

We have been to a **carnival** like this one today. We heard some great music. People dress up to dance and sing at **festivals** all over South Africa.

Love,

Terry

P.S. Mom says that the biggest festival was held when all the people were free to choose the rulers of the country. South Africa became a **democracy** in 1994.

The new South African flag

Dear Ali,

This is the new South African flag. Some of the colors come from the old flag. It was flown when only white people ruled the country. Other colors come from the flag black people flew at that time.

Love,

Karen

P.S. Dad says the leaders who rule the country meet in Cape Town. The other country cities are Pretoria and Bloemfontein.

Glossary

Afrikaans: A language spoken in South Africa based on Dutch

Cape: A piece of land that sticks out into the ocean

Capital: The town or city where people who rule the country meet

Carnival: A special time when people dress up in costumes. They dance in the streets.

Commuter: Someone who travels a distance to and from work each day

Cricket: A ball game played by two teams in a field using a ball and two bats

Crops: Plants that farmers grow

Democracy: A country where all the people choose the leaders they want to run the country

Festival: A time when people celebrate something special or a special time of year

Goods: Things that can be sold

Native: Someone who was born in or connected with a place by birth

Protect: To keep safe from danger

Province: Part of a country that is like a county or a state

P.S.: This stands for Post Script. A postscript is the part of a card or letter that is added at the end, after the person has signed it.

Rugby: A kind of football game

San: Native peoples living in southern Africa who hunt and search for food

Tropics: Hot lands near the middle of the Earth that lie on the map between the Tropic of Capricorn and the Tropic of Cancer

Index

32